THIS BOOK IS

C000046644

....

THE WORLD'S MOST OBNOXIOUS/
DELIGHTFUL/ SEXY/ DISGUSTING/
AWFUL /BEAUTIFUL/VILE/PISCEAN

WITH LOVE FROM / BEST WISHES/
YOURS IN DISGUST ....

P.S. PLEASE TAKE NOTE OF PAGE(S)

....

THE PISCES BOOK

A CORGI BOOK 0 552 12315 3

First publication in Great Britain
PRINTING HISTORY
Corgi edition published 1983
Corgi edition reissued 1984

Copyright © Ian Heath 1983

Conditions of sale
1. This book is sold subject to the condition that it shall not, by
way of trade *or otherwise,* be lent, re-sold, hired out or otherwise
circulated without the publisher's prior consent in any form of
binding or cover other than that in which it is published *and
without a similar condition including this condition being imposed
on the subsequent purchaser.*
2. This book is sold subject to the Standard Conditions of Sale of
Net Books and may not be re-sold in the UK below the net price
fixed by the publishers for the book.

Corgi Books are published by Transworld Publishers Ltd.,
Century House, 61-63 Uxbridge Road, Ealing, London W5 5SA.

Made and printed in Great Britain by the
Guernsey Press Co. Ltd., Guernsey, Channel Islands.

THE PISCES BOOK

BY IAN HEATH

PISCES

FEBRUARY 19 – MARCH 20

TWELFTH SIGN OF THE ZODIAC
SYMBOL : THE FISHES
RULING PLANETS : JUPITER, NEPTUNE
COLOURS : SEA-GREEN, VIOLET
GEMS : OPAL, AQUAMARINE
NUMBER : SEVEN
DAY : THURSDAY
METAL : PLATINUM
FLOWER : GARDENIA

ZZZZZZZZz

The PISCEAN at work...........

.... IS HARD-HEADED..........

.... CAUTIOUS ....

.... DISCIPLINED.................

.... VERY IMAGINATIVE...........

.... A PROBLEM-SOLVER..........

.... LIKES VARIETY..............

.... LOVES GLORY................

... AND COULD CLIMB TO THE TOP.

.............AN AUTHOR.................

......FURNITURE RESTORER........

......TIGHTROPE WALKER........

.... DETECTIVE...............

.... POTTER ....

.... POET..................

.... OR CREATIVE CHEF.

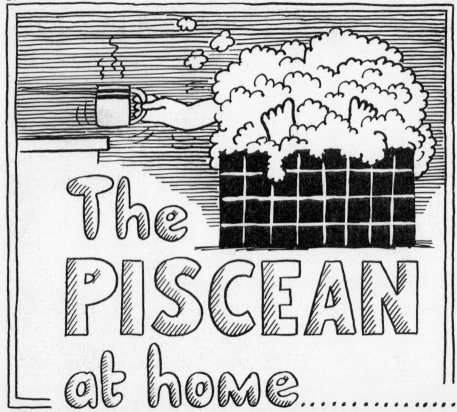

The PISCEAN at home...............

.............LIKES KNITTING............

......DEMANDS CLEANLINESS........

..... AND PERSONAL HYGIENE..........

.......LIKES OPEN FIRES ....

.... PLAYING GAMES..............

.... GOOD FOOD...................

.... MODERN FURNITURE.........

.........ENJOYS PARTIES................

.... MAKING TOAST...............

.....AND GETTING UP EARLY.

..........SPENDING MONEY..........

.........TRAVELLING.............

..........THE THEATRE..................

.... WIDE OPEN SPACES............

DISCOS

..... AND WINTER SPORTS.

..........QUEUEING...................

.... MENDING PUNCTURES.........

.... BEING ALONE.................

.... PIPE SMOKERS..............

.... DARKNESS ....

.... AND ONIONS.

The
PISCEAN
in love...............

...PUTS PARTNER ON A PEDESTAL........

..... CAN BE JEALOUS................

.....NEEDS A STRONG PARTNER.....

.... IS EXCITING................

.... A TALKER ....

.....NOT A DOER....................

.... CAN BE SHY ....

.........DEMONSTRATIVE.................

.... PLAYS HARD TO GET................

............AND CAN'T SLEEP.

PISCEAN

AND PARTNER

HEART RATINGS

♥♥♥♥♥ WOWEE!!
♥♥♥♥ GREAT, BUT NOT 'IT'
♥♥♥ O.K. — COULD BE FUN
♥♥ FORGET IT
♥ WALK QUICKLY THE OTHER WAY

CANCER SCORPIO

CAPRICORN ARIES TAURUS
AQUARIUS

GEMINI PISCES

VIRGO SAGITTARIUS

LEO LIBRA

PISCES PEOPLE

VICTOR HUGO : MICHELANGELO
GEORGE WASHINGTON : HANDEL
ALBERT EINSTEIN : JERRY LEWIS
ALEXANDER GRAHAM BELL
CHOPIN : ELIZABETH TAYLOR

JOHN STEINBECK : ZERO MOSTEL
RUDOLPH NUREYEV : JEAN HARLOW
ELIZABETH BARRETT BROWNING
EDWARD KENNEDY : JOHN ARLOTT
FATS DOMINO : RIMSKI - KORSAKOV
DAVID NIVEN : SIDNEY POITIER
AUGUSTE RENOIR : JOHNNY CASH
PETER FONDA : REX HARRISON
MICHAEL REDGRAVE : NIJINSKY
GEORGE HARRISON : LIZA MINELLI
JACKIE GLEASON : JOHN MILLS